KARI'S SWEET ENCOUNTER WITH THE BIBLE,

THE ORACLES OF GOD

ENGLISH VERSION

BY

STELLA OSAMMOR

Copyright © Published on February 2018
By: Delta Maria Books
2 Hellidon Close
Ardwick,
Manchester
M12 4AH
Telephone: 0161 273 6665
Email: admin@deltamariabooks.com

"Great is the Lord, and GreatLy to be praised

In the city of our God,

In His holy mountain.

Beautiful in elevation,

The joy of the whole earth,

Is Mount Zion on the sides of the north,

The city of the great King.

God is in her palaces;

he is known as her refuge."

- *(PSALM 48:1-3 NKJV)*

Kari loved her job, working as a news reporter for a big TV station was not a job she planned to do for very long. She wanted to be a successful newspaper cartoonist but travelling the world for two to three years as a news reporter she believed, would increase her knowledge of the world and the play of power and politics of the world.

Kari was excited to be going to New Zealand to cover the conference on the World Climate Change and decided she would do a bit of sightseeing after the conference. Kari had been to Australia the year before and had enjoyed the trip immensely. She could not believe her good fortune when her editor told her she would be covering the World Climate Change conference for her TV station.

Kari's beloved Dad had passed away eleven months before. He was a fantastic friend and Dad and it was so hard for everyone in the family to come to terms with his "Going to Glory" (as he often referred to dying).

Kari's mum was now living with her sister Eden, (and her family) in Honolulu. Kari's two brothers; Nicholas and Neil were much older than Kari. They were both married and were living with their families in Surrey.

Kari's mum Olivia was a beautiful fair-skinned woman from French Guiana. She came to live in Britain with her parents when she was just eight, and later trained as paediatric nurse. Olivia met and married Kari's father, Lawrence Ani, an Ibo from Eastern Nigeria just after he finished his training as a paediatrician and began working at the Great Ormond in London. Kari was the youngest child of the family and had been very close to her Dad. He had given Kari his most prized possession just before he died; his threadbare King James Bible. Kari quickly checked her hand bag to see if her dad's Bible was in her hand bag. It smelt of Murray Mints and Old Spice Aftershave. It reminded her so much of her father and helped her cope with the aching void his death had left.

Kari always travelled with two black pencil skirts and several baggy brightly coloured silk shirts and one pair of black denim jeans. She also travelled with high energy biscuits and lots of chocolate, (just in case) the food was strange and unagreeable to her stomach. On this occasion, Kari took her swimsuit and two long evening dresses with her. Several of her colleagues were also planning to do some sightseeing when the conference in Auckland was over.

Kari was taking a connecting flight at Schiphol airport and was just approaching the checking in desk when a mighty explosion blew her back out of the building. Kari gashed her head against a metal barrier and passed out.

Kari's sweet encounter with the Bible, the Oracles of God ▲ 11

Kari found herself travelling rapidly through the starlit sky. She could see the earth way down beneath her. It was an exhilarating sensation and she was enjoying the freedom of being weightless enormously.

Kari's sweet encounter with the Bible, the Oracles of God ▲

Kari looked to her right and saw a beautiful angel with the word 'Gloria' written all over her exquisite robe. Gloria was so beautiful it made Kari want to cry.

'Gloria' nodded and smiled at another angel who flanked Kari on the left. Her name was 'Celeste' and it was written all over her robe. Celeste had dark amazing curls and was a strong and powerful angel. She carried a large flaming sword in her left hand.

Kari knew instinctively that Celeste was a warring angel. She had a dazzling smile and was full of light. Kari trusted the two angels and felt as though she had known them all her life.

Gloria communicated to Kari with great grace and beauty, Gloria was playful, and her laughter was infectious she blew a flute and her antics made Kari laugh like a child. Sometimes, Celeste would leave Kari's side and travel ahead to clear the way of dark clouds and fierce orange balls of fire. Celeste lit the path towards an awesome palace with beautiful starlight and surreal quietness.

Just looking at Gloria, filled Kari with great joy. The music she played on her golden flute was like the sound of many waters and reminded Kari of when she had been in her mother's womb.

Every now and again Gloria would bring up the rear and fill
the heavenly space with the incredible and beautiful music
of her flute.

The angels eventually brought Kari to the gates of the palace. The gates of the palace swung open of its own accord.

Kari's sweet encounter with the Bible, the Oracles of God ▲

And there was Kari's Dad standing hand in hand with Jesus and beaming at her with great joy!!

Kari was enveloped in the embrace of her beloved father who was filled with the same light as Jesus. And then Jesus called Kari by her name! Every core of Kari's being tingled with joy and she began to cry. "I've missed you so much!" she sobbed as Jesus held her close.

Suddenly, Kari found she was alone with Jesus. She was standing in this huge library filled with huge books filled with light. Some of the books were on book shelves and some were on marble work tops and lecterns. Some of the books were opened and some were closed. Light and sparks leapt from the pages of the book. Crystal clear water flowed out of some of the books.

FAITHFULNESS!

JEHOVAH!

JOY!

PEACE!

HALLELUJAH

ETERNAL

GLORY! JOY!

"Kari!" Jesus said looking at her with love. "I have brought you here to tell you about my book".

"Which book?" Kari asked as she gazed in wonder at the fascinating books in the glorious setting.

"The Bible" Jesus said as he held the pages of a huge Bible open. "I gave so many of the words of this precious book to your Dad as gifts. Your Dad loved Psalm 116 especially and always loved to play the opening verse "I love the Lord" to your mum, your siblings and yourself, every Sunday evening after tea."

"Yes! I remember!" Kari said with a big smile "And Mum would sing along as he played it on the piano" Kari recalled those idyllic Surrey summer evenings with joy. The words of the Bibles lived in bubbles and were full of light and life.

Jesus was gentle, his patience was endless, and He spoke with grace. Jesus began to explain that the words in the Bible created mankind and holds the world steadily in place.

"The words of the Bible also light up the spirit of men when they utter them". Kari was fascinated to see how the words linked men on earth to heaven.

Jesus explained that the words of the Bible are full of life and are established settlers of heaven. Jesus quickly turned to Psalm 119 v 89 and showed Kari the Chapter and verse.
Kari was amazed at the way the heart of a child glowed as she read all the verses of Psalm 23 in her grandparents seating room in Tulsa, Arizona.

A little girl in an orphanage in India smiled with joy as a nun read the words of Psalm 27 verse 10, to her before she laid down to sleep. "Though my father and mother forsake me,

thou oh Lord will keep me safe"

A soldier stopped quaking with fear and was filled with the light of heaven as he read the words in the book of Isaiah "When you pass through the waters, I will be with you".

Fear and darkness fled the spirit of men as soon as they spoke the words of the Bible, the precious book of God. Men were flooded with light when they read and pondered the words in the book.

Kari with fascination asked Jesus why people glowed with light every time they uttered the words. "Men are brought into being by the creative force of God's words. The words of God flood the human spirit with its original life and power. The words of God keep the spirit of man strong, fed and filled with life". Jesus said to Kari with urgency. "This is particularly so when they are born anew by the incorruptible seed of my words" (1 Peter Chapter 1 v 23)

"Kari words can fill people with joy, sadness, courage or fear, love or hate, faith or doubt" Jesus continued to explain.

"Kari, words came before everything else in creation. Words give expression to my thoughts and wisdom. Kari, because men have spirits, the words they utter, set spiritual laws into

motion and determine the course of their lives and the lives of the people they love.

Jesus flipped the pages of the huge Bible, in front of Kari and pointed to that part of the book of Proverbs that said; "You are ensnared or taken by the words of your mouth." (Proverbs chapter 6 verse 2)

"My word is the bed rock for the miraculous in the lives of the ones that are mine!"

"Words are building blocks for the creation of relationships. Words can heal, and words can console and can give hope. The words men speak, can destroy or build up lives" Jesus ended softly smiling at the consternation on Kari's face. "I never knew words are so vastly important" Kari turned to say to Jesus.

Jesus got up suddenly and took Kari tightly by the hand. He led her down a long corridor. "Come on Kari, I'll show you around." Jesus said playfully as He opened a huge door with the words 'THE JOYFUL ASSEMBLY OF ANGELS' The door opened into a vast stadium built with white marble. Millions of angels were milling about dancing and singing and praising God with incredible joy. Jesus smiled and closed the huge door firmly shut. Another door had the words "SPIRIT OF RIGHTEOUS MEN MADE PERFECT" The door led into an amazing garden.

"This must be Eden!" Kari whispered with awe. There were several people in the garden, many were around a gurgling stream that produced amazing music. Some sat on smooth white marble benches reading the Bible. So many were full of ecstasy and were ceaselessly singing praises to God. And some were just serenely strolling and enjoying the incredible beauty of Eden.

Kari was captivated by the incredible fragrance of the green shrubs and aroma of lime, mint, orange blossom, and honeysuckle that oozed from the green shrubs at one end of Eden. Kari loved the invigorating fragrance of the shrubs. She inhaled the fragrance deeply, and it made her tingle with life.

Jesus smiled and took Kari firmly by the hand, as he led Kari out of the garden and down a golden corridor. Kari noticed that the corridor glistened because its floor was made of gold! The gold was so pure it looked like glass.

Jesus opened a door along the corridor and it led into a temple with seven lampstands. Jesus led Kari into the outer court of the temple. There was a white fountain that blazed with fire. Thick blood oozed and bubbled out of it. Kari was fascinated! Jesus walked briskly ahead of Kari and brought her to the Holy of Holies.

Suddenly, there was the mercy seat sprinkled with the bright red blood of Jesus. Two cherubim with their hands clasped in prayers arched over the mercy seat. The tips of the wings of the cherubim touched. Kari was awe struck.

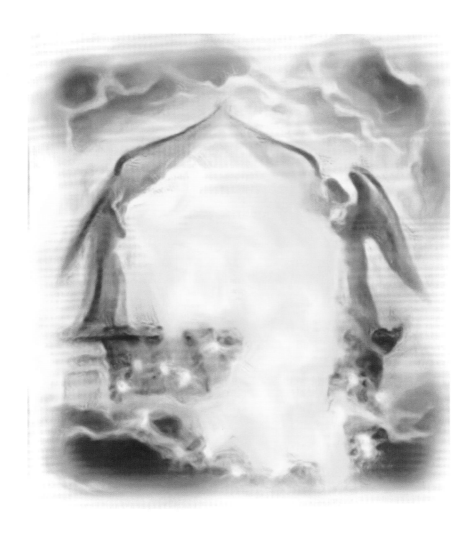

Kari's sweet encounter with the Bible, the Oracles of God

Jesus led Kari back to the corridor. As Jesus opened a white door made of marble and gold, amazing music flowed out of a vast church with millions and millions of people of all races at a church service that went on for eternity. Kari's father was one of the many organists playing amazing worship and praise songs. Everyone wore white translucent robes like the one Jesus wore. The words "FIRST BORN" was written boldly on their robes.

Kari's father waved happily at Kari and Jesus as he continued to play the organ with joyful glee. The music was awesome, and the glory cloud increased the moment Jesus appeared. Jesus sang and danced along with the Church and sparks of glory lights sparked all around him and alighted on the worshippers. The joy and celebration were intense! Kari's spirit fed on it with relish!

Jesus led Kari back to the golden corridor. Jesus held Kari's hand tightly as he opened the door with the words "THE THRONE ROOM" Kari began to weep softly as so much joy flowed from the throne of God towards her. There were soft peals of thunder rumbling from the throne constantly. The one seated on the throne was full of fire and light that dazzled. There was a rainbow arched across the throne, the rainbow came and went. The colours of the rainbow were dazzling and changed all the time. The glorious spectacle changed minute by minute. The glory and beauty of the throne grew in intensity. Everything around the throne moved from one level of glory and translucence to a higher one every time you blinked and looked at it. Kari thought she would collapse with the joy that was coming at her from every direction in the throne room. But the more she looked, the more she herself began to glow and the more she wanted to stay and look.

Kari soon found herself at the banquet room where the marriage supper of the lamb was going to take place. So many angels were busy day and night putting names on chairs and making the room awesome and glorious.

Finally, Jesus slowly led Kari back to the pearly gates where Celeste and Gloria were waiting to lead her back to earth.

Kari's sweet encounter with the Bible, the Oracles of God ▲ **41**

Kari began to wail! "No! no! I am not leaving all this! I am not going back! Jesus No! I'm not leaving you Oh! Jesus! Don't let go of me!" she wailed as Jesus held her in his arms. Celeste and Gloria quickly moved away, as Jesus signalled to them to leave him alone with Kari.

"Hush! Kari Hush!" Jesus said soothingly to Kari as he held her to himself and quietened her with his love! "Hush my precious one!" Jesus said repeatedly.

"You must go for me Kari!" Jesus pleaded after Kari had stopped sobbing. "I promise you I will be here waiting for you. Celeste and Gloria will help you. I will not stop gazing at you by night or by day!" Jesus promised. "See, your face is etched out on my hands! Jesus stretched out his hands, and Kari indeed saw her face beautifully and deeply carved in the palms of Jesus!

"You must go back Kari! That is what you were created for! Go remind men that these words are some of the most pre cious things God has given to mankind. I brought many precious words to the sons of men. The prophets, and so many others, through the help of the Holy Spirit, brought the words of the Bible to men. Kari, I affirmed this in my parting

Jesus with great urgency continued to speak to Kari. "God has given the Bible to men, to guide them back to his heart, and unending victory!"

"Kari, the Father created men from dust! The only aspect of man that is not made of the dust of the earth is the breath of God in man! Tell them Kari! Tell them that men are creatures of God's spoken words and their lives are largely shaped by words for good, or for bad. Tell them Kari! Tell them for me that I am coming for my own very soon!"

"I want them to use the words of the Bible to prepare for my return! I desire to take my own to myself! Tell them about this place I've lovingly made ready for them. Tell them to remember this place! And make this place a crucial part of their earthly lives!"

"Tell them about the mercy seat! Make them understand that God is not angry but wants them to RECEIVE his love for men and wants them to be with him in heaven".

"Tell them about the angels who are waiting day and night to help men win and make it safely home to the Father!"

"Tell them about the Church of the first born, which proves that God sees his rebirthed sons and daughters as heirs of all he owns! Tell them to RECEIVE his love! Tell them that through my death and suffering, I have faithfully negotiated a father and son relationship between my father and all who RECEIVE me as a BLOOD BROTHER!

"I desire my brethren and sisters to be in their millions and from every race and tongue! Tell them about the peace that you saw resting upon the spirits of the righteous men made perfect. And the great example they are to the pilgrim soul!"

"Tell them my father's heart is full of love! But the deeds of all men must be laid open for all to see. My blood WILL SPEAK MERCY! If they allow it to avail for them!"

"This is Zion and as it says in Hebrews chapter 12 verse 18 to 22. I LONG FOR MY BRIDE THE CHURCH! My beloved! that are called by name! Co-heirs with me of everything the father owns! Those who are united to me in spirit!"

Kari's heart raced and pounded in her chest with great force. Her eyes gazed deep into the eyes of Jesus all the time he spoke to her. All Jesus said registered itself in Kari's spirit. Kari however prayed with desperation that Jesus would change his mind and ask her to stay! Her eyes searched the eyes of Jesus, hoping that he would relent and allow her to remain with him.

"But where do I find the words to tell them about the beauty of your love?" Kari wailed as a fresh wave of sorrow engulfed her soul. "Where do I find the words to tell them about the delight of your company?" Kari asked Jesus as floods of tears began to course down her cheeks again.

"Kari, you mustn't leave this place thinking I've rejected you! My heart aches for you to stay! Please trust me and be brave for me my precious child!! I will follow you everywhere with my eyes" Jesus promised and held Kari's intense gaze with his own. Kari suddenly crashed herself down at the feet of Jesus and began sobbing with all her might.

Jesus quickly bent down and hoisted Kari into his arms as he began to pray for her with intensity! Kari rested her head against Jesus as he calmed her troubled spirit. "Peace Kari! I speak my peace into your spirit! Peace like a river! Joy! My Joy and gladness, instead of this heaviness!"

"My Peace! My Peace!" Jesus repeated as Kari's anguish ebbed away…"Come, I must show you something" Jesus said quietly after a while.

Jesus took Kari gently by the hand and led Kari to a round giant table with a crystal clear circular screen in the middle of it. Jesus made the screen come very close; so, Kari could see the images in the screen.

"Mum! Eden! Nicholas! Neil!" Kari called out to her family as they stood around her hospital bed crying. Kari's mum had

SAVIOUR
AND
MIGHTY
ROCK

SAVIOUR
AND
MIGHTY
ROCK

her head buried in Kari's chest sobbing.

"Your mum has been sobbing none stop for five days. She has been storming heaven with all sorts of prayers, begging the Father to send you back to her!".

"God gave you to your Mum because of the overwhelming grief your Mother felt when her Mother, your Nan, Amy died and returned here in glory. We can't have your mother bury you Kari! You must go back to them my precious child!".
"Kari, I will be here waiting for you!

"Kari, Kari, Kari" Jesus said softly as Kari began plunging back into her body.

The heart monitor bleeped as Kari jolted fully back into her body. "She's back! My precious angel is back!" Kari's mum whispered in a hoarse, croaky, voice.

"Dr Barker! Dr Barker!" Eden ran out calling as she alerted the hospital staff at the nurses' bay at the intensive care unit. Nicholas and Neil rammed their fists into the emergency call buttons sobbing with joy and then embraced their Mother in turn.

Kari smiled at her siblings and mother's enormous joy! Kari whispered to her sister "Eden, where is my Bible?"
"Right here honey, right here" Eden said as she handed Kari their father's threadbare Bible.

A week later, Kari was strong enough to travel back to Neil's home in Surrey with her mum and Eden.

Just before Thanksgiving, Kari travelled with her mum to Eden's idyllic home in Honolulu.

Eden and her mum Olivia listened with rapture as Kari told them about her time with Jesus and everything He told and showed her in heaven.

A year later Kari's mum returned to Glory! Beautiful Olivia Ani, the wife of Lawrence Ani, Kari's beloved mum, died peacefully in her sleep.

After her mother's funeral, Kari began to write this amazing account of how she went to heaven and was instructed by Jesus to tell the world about the beauty of heaven, the ardour and longing Jesus has for his own and the beauty of the precious words of God, contained in the book we call the Bible.

THE END

Dear Reader,

Have you ever made Jesus the Lord and Saviour of your life?

If not, please say the prayer below and commit your life to Jesus so you can live with him in the bliss of heaven at the end of your life here on earth.

PRAYER OF SALVATION

Dear God,

I come to you in the name of Jesus. I confess that I need to be right with you.

I ask you to please forgive me all my sins and accept me as your own.

The Bible says that if I confess with my mouth that "JESUS IS LORD" and BELIEVE in my heart that God raised him up from the dead, I will be saved .

I believe in my heart and confess with my mouth that JESUS IS LORD AND SAVIOUR OF MY LIFE!

I thank you Jesus for saving me!

I am so happy that I am now yours!

Amen!

If you prayed the prayer of salvation and committed your life to Christ please email us at: delta.maria@btinternet.com and share your testimony with us.

If your church group would want to use this book in a revival, evangelism or outreach programme material ; please email us at: admin@deltamariabooks.com.

May God bless you.

The adventure of a lifetime might just be closer than you think!
Delta Maria write with such gusto and story-telling flair
that draw you into a vivid experience of the rich African culture.

Each book captures the beauty and triumph of diversity
served up in thoughtful nuggets of joy and emotion.
Now available from Amazon, the popular books
have been translated into French and Spanish.

**A fantastic educational resource for school children
and fun-loving adults alike.**